Y0-BZE-524

To Be Me

Written by Rebecca Etlinger

Illustrated by Mark Tomassi

This book is dedicated to
helping children understand
Asperger's Syndrome.

cts

WPS Creative Therapy Store™

Published by

WPS Creative Therapy Store™

12031 Wilshire Boulevard

Los Angeles, California 90025

www.creativetherapystore.com

International Standard Book Number: 978-087424-452-6

1 2 3 4 5 6 7 8 9

When starting to think about my Master's Thesis, I never dreamed that it would turn into something with the potential to help so many children. This project would not have been possible without the help and support of so many people in my life. First of all, I would like to thank my family for supporting me (both emotionally and financially) throughout graduate school. I would not be who I am today if it weren't for my parents always urging me to strive for more and my brothers serving as a constant source of laughter. The Hermans and the Richardsons also have a huge spot in my heart and I treasure the times we spend together.

I need to thank all my professors, especially Ginny C., Paul M., and Jennifer L. at the Rochester Institute of Technology, who introduced me to the field of School Psychology and who inspired me to reach for new opportunities and constantly challenge myself.

Finally, I would like to thank Mark Tomassi for illustrating this book. As a college student, he took on this extra project solely to gain experience for himself. He worked around my deadlines and never complained about my editing changes. I will forever be thankful to him for helping make my book a reality.

Rebecca Etlinger

Hi, my name is David, and I am 10 years old.

I have blond hair and blue eyes, two arms and two legs. I'm just an average-looking kid. I live in a house with my mommy, daddy and my little sister Mary. We always do fun stuff together, like going to the park and baseball games. When I grow up, I want to be a race-car driver.

As you can see, I am just a regular kid, except for one thing.

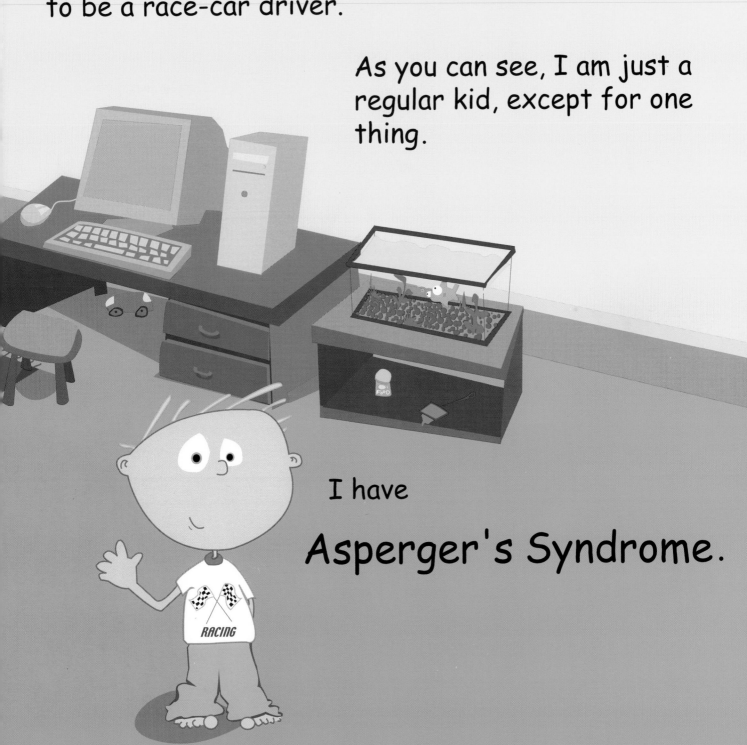

I have

Asperger's Syndrome.

I am in the fourth grade now, but growing up I always felt different from the other kids in my class. It was hard for me when I was younger because I never understood why. Talking with my parents and teachers helped me realize that everyone is unique.

Some kids have different color skin.

BUS STOP

Some wear braces or glasses.

Sometimes there are also differences on the inside. Some kids don't speak English, and other kids are very good at math. They take classes in another classroom.

My mom says that everyone's brain works differently. Unlike me, some kids need to go to the nurse's office during lunch to take medicine. The medicine helps them concentrate in school. Even though I might think in a different way, I still like to do the same things as other kids. I am friends with most of the kids in my class, even those who wear glasses.

Things in my life are great now, but school wasn't always easy for me. My kindergarten teacher, Mrs. Richards, told my parents that she was worried about me. I didn't have any friends and I spent a lot of time alone.

When I did talk to other kids, I only talked about cars. Most kids got bored after 5 minutes. Mrs. Richards said that I was a smart boy, but that I had a hard time playing and talking with the other kids.

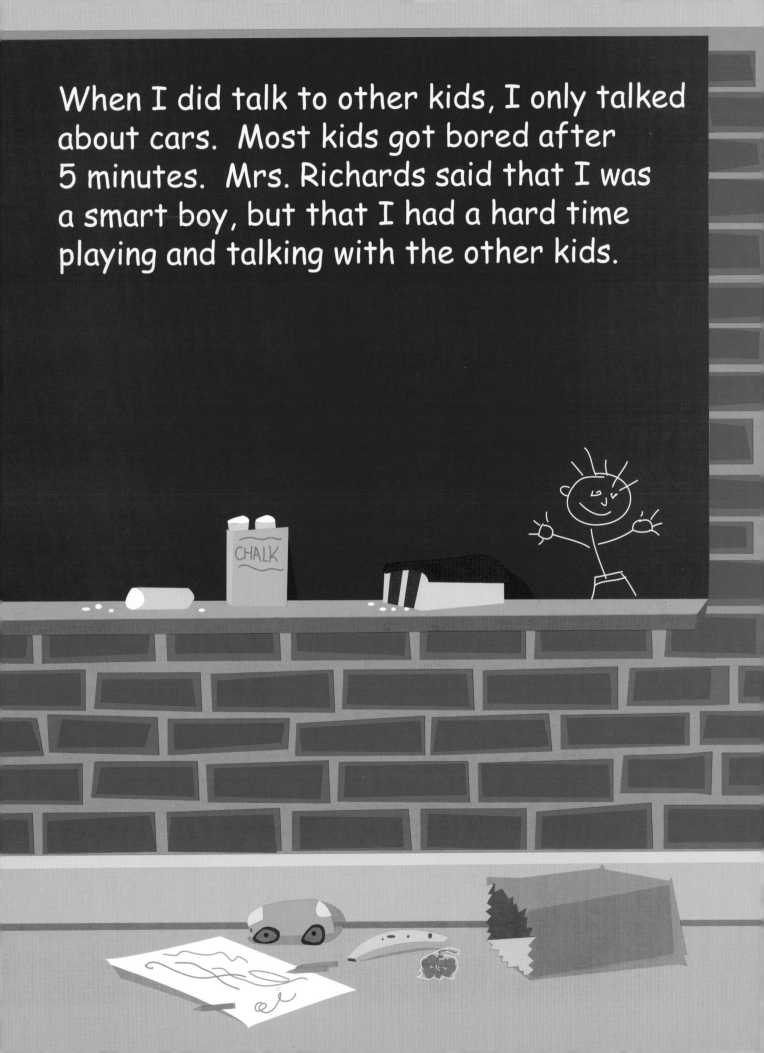

I remember one time at the beginning of the year in gym class, I was playing catch with Andy. When I tried to catch the ball, I missed, and the ball hit me right on the head. I looked so silly when that happened.

My head hurt so much and I had a bump for a week. Some kids started to laugh, which made me feel embarrassed!

Another time in third grade I had to be partners with Sara, a girl in my class. She had never talked to me before, and she got upset when she found out she had to be my partner. "I don't want to be partners with him," she said. "He is so weird." This hurt my feelings and made me feel sad.

I began to think that the other kids were right when they said mean things about me.

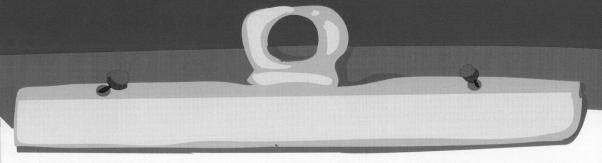

NAME _ David _ _ _ _   AGE _ 9 _ _   WEIGHT 62 lbs.

SYMPTOMS

Mrs. Herman, my third-grade teacher, noticed that I was alone a lot and that I didn't talk to other kids. She decided to talk to my parents because she wanted me to get some help. My parents said that they had seen the same things. After talking for a while, my parents decided to take me to see Dr. Groon.

When I got to the doctor's office, I was scared that I was going to have to get a shot or something worse, but seeing the doctor wasn't bad at all. After I took some tests and played some games, the doctor told us that I had Asperger's Syndrome.

At first I was really upset and afraid, and I wondered if I was going to die. My doctor assured me that I was going to live a long and happy life. Once he explained Asperger's Syndrome to me, I felt a lot better. I finally knew why I had difficulty making friends and playing with kids in school. I think it's important for all kids to know about Asperger's Syndrome because those of us who have it are just kids who want to have friends, like everyone else.

About Me

I have bad handwriting, and sometimes I have a hard time reading what I have written. I do not have good balance, and sometimes I am a little clumsy. I also have a hard time running and playing sports.

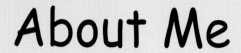

Having a conversation

I love to talk about cars. Sometimes I don't realize that other people might like to talk about something else. I don't mean to be rude; I just have a hard time figuring out when I should talk.

ME

Daily routines
1. Must clean room.
2. Have to play soccer.

Making friends

I have a harder time than most kids making friends, but that doesn't mean I don't want to have friends. When I was younger, I wasn't even sure what it actually meant to be a friend. Just be patient with me, and I'll show you what a good friend I can be.

Rules for Tag
1. Always count to 10.
2. Never more than 5 people.

I like to play games with other kids—mostly tag and race-car driver. But I like to have things my own way. I usually like to make up rules, and I might get upset when they aren't followed. That doesn't mean you can't play with me. Just work with me to figure out the rules.

After the doctor told my parents that I had Asperger's Syndrome, they went to my school to talk to my class. They told the other kids that I wanted to have friends and gave them some ideas about how to talk with me. Kids in my class were also given ideas about what kind of games we could play together, and now they ask me to play with them.

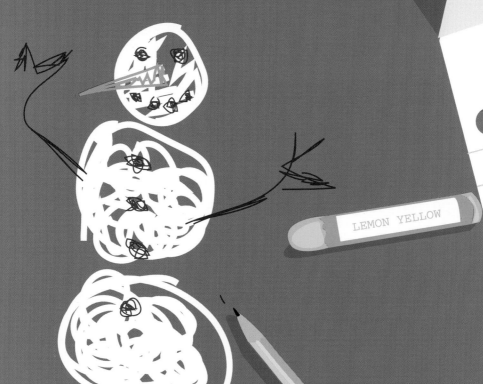

LEMON YELLOW

FOREST GREEN

Here are some drawings of things that I like........

Here are some things you can do to help a classmate with Asperger's Syndrome:

Understand that the teacher might give some students extra attention once in a while. Teaching can be hard when there is only one teacher and many kids who learn differently.

$$1+1+1= 3$$

$$+ \quad + \quad =3$$

Ask a student with Asperger's Syndrome to join in games on the playground or in the classroom. Even if he doesn't know how to play the game, he can learn if you explain the rules.

home base

1. count for 10 sec before leaving tree.
2. must arrive to safety after leaving tree.

safety

Ask a kid with Asperger's Syndrome to come over to your house to play after school. You might have the same hobbies and play the same games.

Dan's
HOUSE
555-6294

When there is a new kid in the class, explain to him or her about Asperger's Syndrome. Remember, kids with this disorder really want to have friends to play with. Even though they seem different, don't forget that they have feelings like everyone else.

SCHOOL BUS

I was happy that my parents had talked to my classmates because the kids were so much nicer to me afterward. I found kids to play with, and I didn't have to play alone anymore. After learning about Asperger's Syndrome, the other kids stopped being scared and began including me in their activities.

One boy named Dan asked me to come over to his house to play after school. We played hide and seek until it got dark outside. He didn't even get mad when I made up some of the rules. We had such a fun time playing together!

Also, that girl Sara who had once made fun of me was in my fourth-grade class. After learning about Asperger's Syndrome, she realized that it wasn't nice to call me names, and she actually asked to be my science partner.

4th-Grade Science Fair

Having Asperger's Syndrome makes me unique in my class. I don't know why I was born with it, but my mom says it's because I am special. My life is great now, especially since all the other kids in school have learned about Asperger's Syndrome. I can't wait to grow up and become a race-car driver, but right now I need to focus on finishing the fourth grade.